HOW TO TAKE CARE OF YOUR PET

DINOSAUR

YOUR PET
DIPLODOCUS

By Kirsty Holmes

THE
OFFICIAL
F.O.S.S.I.L
GUIDE

THE SECRET BOOK COMPANY

©2019

The Secret Book Company

King's Lynn
Norfolk PE30 4LS

ISBN: 978-1-912502-41-7

All rights reserved

Printed in Malaysia

A catalogue record for this book is available from the British Library.

Written by:
Kirsty Holmes

Edited by:
Madeline Tyler

Designed by:
Danielle Jones

All facts, statistics, web addresses and URLs in this book were verified as valid and accurate at time of writing. No responsibility for any changes to external websites or references can be accepted by either the author or publisher.

IMAGE CREDITS

Cover – solar22, Bibela, ONYXprj, stuckmotion, isaree, Kurt Natalia. 1 & throughout – stuckmotion, solar22. 5 – Panda Vector, robuart, artbesouro, azalai, eatcute. 6 – Sentavio. 7 – Vetreno. 8 – Lorelyn Medina, Graphic Treasure. 10 – Natali Snailcat, HQ Vectors Premium Studio, totallyjamie, elenabsl. 11 – Natali Snailcat, VectoRaith, Incomible. 12 – Rohatynchuk Mykola, BigMouse. 14–15 – robuart, chuckchee, nemlaza. 17 – DECTER. 18 – Vectors Bang. 20 – MicroOne, ZenStockers, Rvector. 21 – Creative Mood. 22 – Lemberg Vector studio. Images are courtesy of Shutterstock.com. With thanks to Getty Images, Thinkstock Photo and iStockphoto.

CONTENTS

THE OFFICIAL FOSSIL GUIDE

Words that look like <u>this</u> can be found in the glossary on page 24.

F.O.S.S.I.L

So, you're the proud owner of a dinosaur egg. Congratulations!

Owning a pet dinosaur is a lot of hard work, but it's worth the trouble. Dinosaurs make excellent pets.

Per 1
Gn +1
C6/M7
P5/E2
M1 1.3

CONGRATULATIONS! IT'S A... DIPLODOCUS!

If you are a first-time dinosaur owner, you probably have lots of questions. Never fear! This handy F.O.S.S.I.L guide will tell you all you need to know.

F.O.S.S.I.L
FACT

F.O.S.S.I.L stands for:

Federal
Office of
Super
Sized
Interesting
Lizards

HOW TO TAKE CARE OF YOUR PET
DINOSAUR
YOUR PET
DIPLODOCUS

THE
OFFICIAL
F.O.S.S.I.L
GUIDE

EGGS

Diplodocus (say: dip-LOD-er-cus) eggs are quite small for their enormous size. The eggs are shaped like a rugby ball. They are about 30 centimetres (cm) long, and 25 cm across.

25 CM

30 CM

Diplodocus eggs should stay quite cool. The best place to keep your egg is in an underground <u>nest</u>.

YOUR EGG WILL TAKE BETWEEN 65 AND 82 DAYS TO <u>HATCH</u>.

BABIES

Diplodocus babies are known as "sauropodlets" (say: saw-oh-pod-lets). When yours hatches, it may be up to one metre (m) long!

BABIES HAVE SHORTER NECKS, WHICH WILL GET LONGER AS YOUR PET GROWS.

Feed your sauropodlet <u>mosses</u> and ferns. A sauropodlet needs to gain two kilograms (kg) in weight every day, so make sure you have plenty of its favourite foods.

GROWTH

Your sauropodlet will grow very quickly. By the time it is a year old, it should reach around 3 m in length and weigh the same as a cow.

BIRTH

6 MONTHS

ADULT

FIRST BIRTHDAY

Adults can grow as long as 32 m, from nose to tail. Don't worry about fitting it into your house, though. Your Diplodocus will be happy to sleep outside.

FOOD

Diplodocus are <u>herbivores</u>.
They have teeth like little pegs,
perfect for stripping leaves from
branches and ferns.

<u>CYCADS</u>

BUSHES

TREES

FERNS

<u>GINGKOES</u>

A huge dinosaur like the Diplodocus needs to eat an enormous amount of food every day to survive. You will need to plan ahead to make sure that you have enough food each day.

EXERCISE

Your Diplodocus will need to go for daily walks. Lucky for you, they are big and heavy, so they can't walk very fast – you should be able to keep up on foot.

FOSSIL FACT

Your Diplodocus will take big steps on its massive FIVE METRE legs – so take care not to get squashed!

8 – 15 KILOMETRES PER HOUR (KPH)

Although Diplodocus have long necks, they can't lift their heads very high. You will need a long lead for walks – around eight metres should be enough if your Diplodocus is well-trained.

8M

NAMING

Naming your Diplodocus is very important when <u>bonding</u> with your pet. You could choose to use part of the Diplodocus's name as a nickname.

DIPPY

F.O.S.S.I.L FACT

What will you name your Diplodocus?

You could use words that describe your Diplodocus to name it instead. Diplodocus has a long neck and tail, and is very large.

THIS OWNER NAMED HER PET "STRETCH" BECAUSE OF ITS LONG NECK.

STRETCH!

WASHING

Pets must be kept clean and well-groomed. Diplodocus are very large. To wash properly behind their ears, you will need:

A RAINCOAT

GOGGLES

A LADDER

A LONG HOSEPIPE

A BROOM

WELLIES

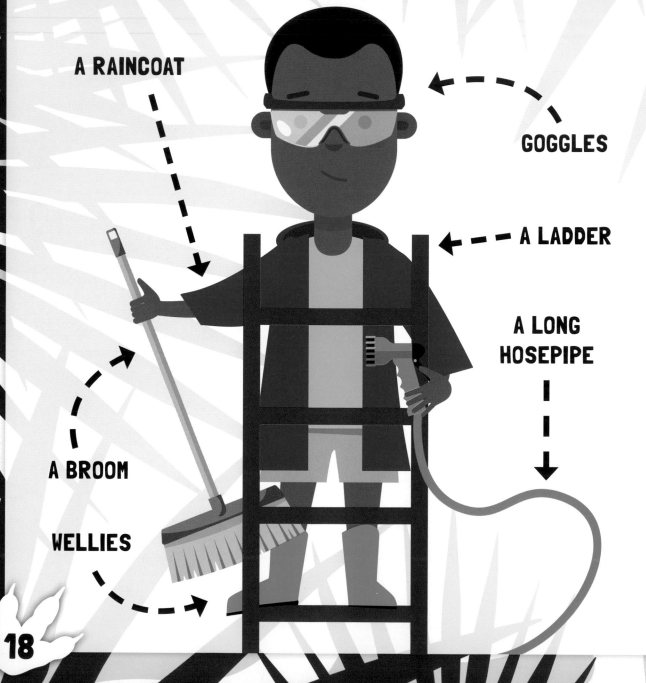

Make sure you clean its teeth! Your Diplodocus will lose many teeth over its lifetime, but don't worry. It will grow new teeth to replace them in about 35 days.

PROBLEMS

Such a large pet, eating such huge meals, will produce a lot of poo. A Diplodocus can produce over 70 kg of poo every day – this will fill up five bin bags.

DINOSAUR POO MAKES EXCELLENT <u>FERTILISER</u>.

Diplodocus like to wander off. Make sure you teach your sauropodlet some simple commands. A Diplodocus loose in the neighbourhood could cause a lot of unwanted damage.

DIPPY, STAY!

TRICKS

The Diplodocus's long neck makes it perfect for a game of throw-and-catch.

DON'T PLAY CATCH IN A CROWDED AREA. PEOPLE COULD GET SQUISHED.

Train your Diplodocus to lift you up on its head. The Diplodocus should easily be able to lift you into the treetops. Make sure you hold on tight!

THERE ARE HOURS OF FUN TO BE HAD WITH YOUR FRIENDLY NEW PET!

23

GLOSSARY

BONDING   forming a close relationship

CYCADS   an ancient species of very spiky tree, like a palm tree

FERTILISER   substances added to plants and crops to help them grow

GINGKOES   an ancient species of tree with tasty seeds

HATCH   when a baby creature emerges from its egg

HERBIVORES   animals that only eat plants

MOSSES   small flowerless plants which grow in clumps

NEST   any place used by an animal to lay eggs or rear young

INDEX